DESPERATE  TIMES

Peter Brookes

\B^b\

Biteback Publishing

For Angela

First published in Great Britain in 2021 by
Biteback Publishing Ltd, London
Copyright © Peter Brookes 2021

Individual illustrations featured in this book were first published in *The Times*.

ISBN 978-1-78590-688-6

10 9 8 7 6 5 4 3 2 1

A CIP catalogue record for this book is available from the British Library.

Set in Baskerville

Printed and bound in Great Britain by
CPI Group (UK) Ltd, Croydon CR0 4YY

INTRODUCTION

'DON'T YOU KNOW THERE'S A WAR ON?' 'HOW DARE YOU QUESTION THE PM?' 'WHERE'S YOUR SENSE OF PATRIOTISM?' Just a few of the brickbats hurled in my direction when the pandemic reached these shores and I started to target cartoons at a wholly unprepared and complacent government. The flaws were all too soon apparent to most of us: ministers still shaking hands, not social distancing despite the scientific advice, completely botching PPE, late with lockdown… the list goes on. Less than a year on, administering a drubbing to the woeful, cack-handed Johnson government would not seem at all undeserved as we passed the appalling landmark figure of 100,000 deaths, so many of them shamefully avoidable.

It would be wrong not to give credit where it is due, however, and of course the vaccine rollout has been a massive success. It may yet give Johnson his get-out-of-jail card, although it cannot absolve him from any of the above. But even as they have got the vaccine programme so spectacularly right, they still get other things spectacularly wrong. Choosing trade over lives is one such, by failing to close the UK's borders to travellers from India in the face of the Delta variant in order to facilitate a deal with Modi.

This collection of cartoons is something of a before and after: before Covid, when 'normal' politics held sway and I could vary the subject matter in any given week, and after Covid, when I've hardly been able to get away from it in well over a year. We have all been fixated on Covid – understandably when it's a matter of life and death. I used to think I was a single-issue cartoonist because Brexit was all-consuming for so long, but this has been something else. Trying to make a point about, say, Keir Starmer's stuttering leadership of the Labour Party cuts little ice when people are exclusively focused on hospitals and care homes in crisis, though as you can see, I've certainly tried.

There have been moments when news stories have broken which have been too important to be overshadowed by Covid and I've hungrily drawn them, sometimes with a sense of sheer relief: the Cameron lobbying scandal, the return of rioting in Northern Ireland, the great Salmond–Sturgeon bust-up. I have worried, though, that in this period I've not been able to give as much attention to particular outrages as they warrant: Myanmar; the fates of Hong Kong and the Uighurs at the hands of China; Navalny's persecution by Putin in Russia; the eleven-day Israel–Palestine conflict. Furthermore, there are only a niggardly two or three cartoons on climate change, which is surely more of an existential threat than Covid. And if I can sense this neglect in my small corner, I'm sure it means these issues are similarly overlooked on a global scale, all because of the pandemic. They may even be happening because of it; far easier to club a pro-democracy protester when the world is looking the other way.

Apart from the changes to *what* I draw, *how* I draw has also altered significantly. Like many others, I was quickly required to work from home because of my age and 'vulnerable' categorisation. I had always worked at the *Times* offices, with all the advantages that gave me, including close working with colleagues and all the technical help needed to get my drawings onto the page and online. I'm hardly on my own, though, when my wife Angela generously and ably gets me out of the holes I dig for myself.

My working day starts when I'm woken at 6.25 by the *Today* programme, then it's a diet of news before, during and after breakfast, until it's time for my daily exercise regime of five flights of stairs to my studio at the top of the house. There, my brain is given a workout as I go a few rounds wrestling with the beginnings of a cartoon idea. At 10.15, it's time to sign in for morning conference at *The Times* by phone. But first there's a pre-conference conference, a very useful fifteen-minute talking shop of section heads from which I take what is on the paper's collective mind on any given day. The hour or so following this is morning conference proper, a more structured affair giving the breakdown of what is planned for each section of the paper. The early start risks the schedule being upended by those bigger and better news stories which might break later in the day, but even so it's a richly informative source from which to gather material for an eventual cartoon.

Coming up with the idea is always the hardest part of the process. Getting all worked up at some sleazeball politician on the take with PPE, say, isn't always of itself enough to get an idea up and running. You can gaze into space hoping the damned thing just pops out, or you can stare despairingly at the white sheet of paper in front of you, chewing pencils down to the stub, until finally, at last, the solution emerges. Even then, you may think you know what you want to say, but transposing that onto paper can sometimes be like getting blood out of a stone. But once I've got there, I'll photograph the sketched result and email it to the Comment editor, who'll then discuss it with me. Once we are both happy, it's a question of drawing it (pen, ink and watercolour) in what time is left. Over the years, judging how much to put into a drawing with the time available has become an artform in itself. Avoiding a mad dash towards the 7.30 deadline (which could compromise the drawing) is the objective, and in the main, somehow it happens. I'm often asked, 'Do you ever run out of ideas?' or 'Have you an idea kept up your sleeve, just in case?' The answer to both is 'no'. In the first instance, you always come up with something, because you can't leave half a page of the newspaper empty at the end of the day. You may on occasion wish for that 'something' to have been much better, but you thank your lucky stars you can live to fight another day. In the second instance, an old idea kept in

reserve will never have the necessary freshness of the moment. So if you do have something up your sleeve, best to leave it there.

Political cartoons will regularly draw criticism arising from confusion. Those same members of the previously mentioned 'HOW DARE YOU' brigade will rail at your attempts to tackle a subject as bleak as the pandemic because they deem it to be outside the scope of mere cartoons. A cartoon is supposed to be funny, they say, and you are cruelly laughing at tragedy. Well, it's not as simple as that. Cartoons can have serious intent. They can laugh in the face of tragedy, not at it, which is the basis of much black humour. A laugh morphs into a wince. Of course, a political cartoon can often aim to raise a laugh pure and simple. After all, if you can't laugh at political failure, what can you laugh at?

I'm one of the lucky ones. I've not succumbed to the pandemic, nor have I lost close friends or family members. In fact, I gained one, becoming a delighted grandfather for the third time. I've not lost my job, nor been furloughed. I've been able to set my face against this hideous disease, not in as meaningful a way as healthcare professionals or workers in essential services, but at least I've engaged with it regularly as a cartoonist. I was born in a world war but have never been close to terrible events in my adult life before. Until now. It has been a strange privilege.

Photos emerge showing Prince Andrew partying with Jeffrey Epstein, while Boris Johnson's advice to prorogue Parliament for an unprecedented five weeks during the Brexit crisis embroils the Queen in controversy.

Dominic Cummings's role in the expulsion of twenty-one Conservative rebels opposed to a no-deal Brexit causes dissent in the Tory ranks. The Prime Minister and his partner adopt a puppy.

Boris Johnson proceeds with plans to prorogue Parliament as MPs fight to prevent
a no-deal Brexit. The Zimbabwean 'liberator and oppressor' Robert Mugabe dies.

Deputy Labour leader Tom Watson's call for the party to 'unequivocally back Remain' puts him at odds with leader Jeremy Corbyn's policy of renegotiating a Brexit deal before calling a referendum.

Boris Johnson faces calls to resign after his suspension of Parliament is deemed unlawful. Donald Trump, undergoing his first impeachment inquiry, says the PM is 'not going anywhere'.

Boris Johnson dismisses pleas to avoid using language that could incite violence towards MPs. Meanwhile, a senior Cabinet minister warns, 'Deliver Brexit or face riots.'

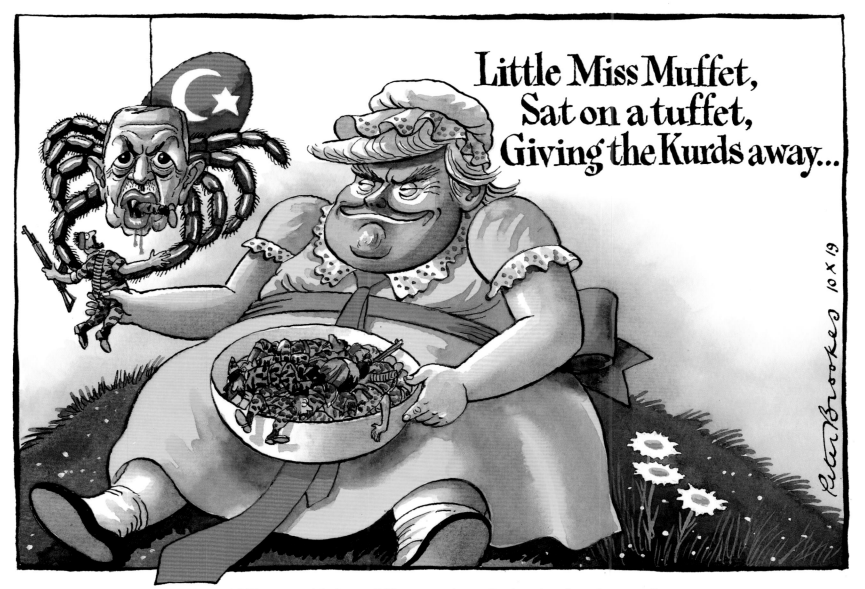

Little Miss Muffet,
Sat on a tuffet,
Giving the Kurds away...

Donald Trump withdraws US troops from Syria, clearing the way for
Turkey's offensive against US-backed Kurdish fighters.

Thirty-nine people are found dead in a refrigerated lorry in Essex, highlighting the plight of migrants, refugees and victims of human trafficking.

Despite opinion polls predicting a Conservative victory, Jeremy Corbyn backs an early general election, with one Labour MP calling the decision 'sheer madness'.

MYANMAR...

Myanmar's leader Aung San Suu Kyi defends the military's actions towards Rohingya Muslims and rejects allegations of genocide despite claims of mass murder, sexual violence and displacement.

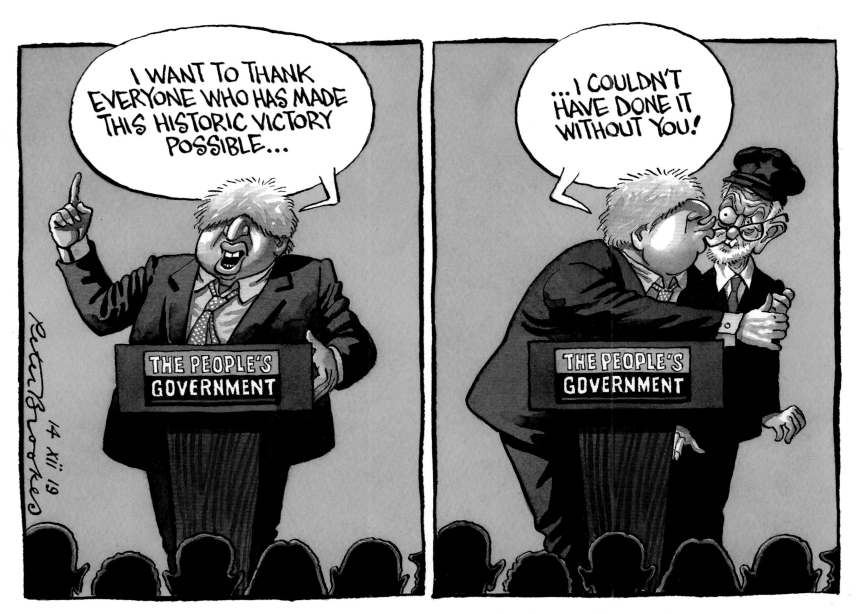

The Conservative Party achieves a comfortable victory in the general election, winning a number of Labour heartland seats.

As thousands flee Australia's apocalyptic bushfires, its conservative government downplays the link with climate change and rejects calls to downsize the fossil fuel industries.

Following the bombshell announcement that Prince Harry and Meghan Markle are stepping back from the royal family, reports emerge that the couple have applied to trademark the Sussex Royal brand.

Vladimir Putin announces a series of constitutional reforms shifting power away from the presidency, prompting speculation about his plans for the end of his presidential term in 2024.

The UK officially leaves the EU at 11 p.m. on 31 January 2020. Boris Johnson
turns his attention to negotiating a trade deal with the US.

The death of whistleblower Dr Li Wenliang, who was punished for trying to raise the alarm about coronavirus, sparks grief and anger at the Chinese government's response to the crisis.

Boris Johnson faces down a Tory rebellion as he confirms that the controversial HS2 high-speed rail link will go ahead despite a backlash at the increasing costs and management failures.

Social care leaders warn that the government's plans to deny visas to so-called 'low-skilled' workers after Brexit will put the elderly and vulnerable at risk.

Communities devastated by flooding criticise Boris Johnson for failing to visit the worst-hit areas and declining to call an emergency COBRA meeting.

Boris Johnson warns of a 'substantial period of disruption' due to coronavirus, while shoppers begin to stockpile loo roll.

Peter Brookes 13 iii 20

Donald Trump announces sweeping travel restrictions in a bid to stop the spread of the
'foreign virus', telling Americans, 'This virus will not have a chance against us.'

Health Secretary Matt Hancock evokes the spirit of the Blitz, comparing Britain's fight against coronavirus to enemy bombings during the Second World War.

Politicians join the public in Clap for Carers, thanking NHS staff for their service – but many see it as an empty gesture given key workers' lack of PPE.

With the UK struggling to roll out coronavirus testing, the government admits that only 2,000 NHS workers have been tested, meaning thousands must self-isolate and cannot work.

As Rishi Sunak expands the coronavirus loan scheme for large businesses, Captain Tom Moore, a 99-year-old war veteran, raises millions for the NHS by walking 100 lengths of his garden.

Controversy continues around the shortage of PPE, while lockdown is extended for 'at least three weeks'.

SOCIAL DISTANCING: AT LAST, A USE FOR REES-MOGG...

23 iv 20

Peter Brookes

Parliament returns for hybrid proceedings, with even arch-traditionalist
Jacob Rees-Mogg in favour of allowing MPs to join via video link.

MAKE YOUR OWN FACEMASKS FROM SPARE MATERIAL...

While official guidance on face masks remains under review, senior doctors encourage the public to wear homemade face coverings amid ongoing NHS shortages of PPE.

Matt Hancock repeatedly refuses to apologise for mistakes on PPE provision after a BBC *Panorama* investigation discovers that the government failed to buy vital equipment to handle a pandemic.

As the government watches the Covid-19 R number, Boris Johnson and Carrie Symonds welcome their first child – but the PM remains tight-lipped on the number of children he actually has.

DEATHS: UK PASSES ITALY...

7 V 20 Peter Brookes

The UK's coronavirus death toll passes Italy's, making it the highest in Europe.

China announces plans to impose sweeping new national security laws on Hong Kong, in effect
eroding Hong Kong's autonomy under the 'one country, two systems' agreement.

While thousands around the world gather in solidarity with widespread US protests after the murder of George Floyd by US police officers, Donald Trump threatens to deploy the military.

Boris Johnson faces criticism for his slowness to respond on issues ranging
from Covid-19 to the Black Lives Matter movement.

The Office for National Statistics reveals that the UK's GDP fell by a record 20.4 per cent in April 2020, the first full month of lockdown.

UEFA meets to discuss plans for football tournaments delayed by coronavirus. Public confidence in the government continues to plummet as a result of its handling of the pandemic.

Ed Miliband, who presided over Labour's 2015 election defeat,
co-authors a post-mortem on the party's disastrous 2019 result.

Boris Johnson's woes continue, with Education Secretary Gavin Williamson coming under fire for his handling of schools, and Housing Secretary Robert Jenrick referred to Parliament's sleaze watchdog.

FAMILIAR CHINESE PATTERN...

Protests erupt in Hong Kong when the controversial new security law enters into force. Hundreds are arrested, with the police firing rubber bullets, teargas and water cannons into the crowds.

Boris Johnson urges the public to 'act responsibly' as pubs reopen in the latest stage of lockdown easing. Dominic Cummings remains in post following his flouting of lockdown rules.

THE GOOD THE BAD and THE UGLY

7 vii 20 Peter Brookes
— RIP ENNIO MORRICONE

Rishi Sunak outshines his boss as he prepares to announce new spending
plans. Ennio Morricone dies aged ninety-one.

Rishi Sunak is tipped as a Prime Minister in waiting after unveiling his £30 billion summer
statement, including plans to create jobs and introduce a stamp duty holiday.

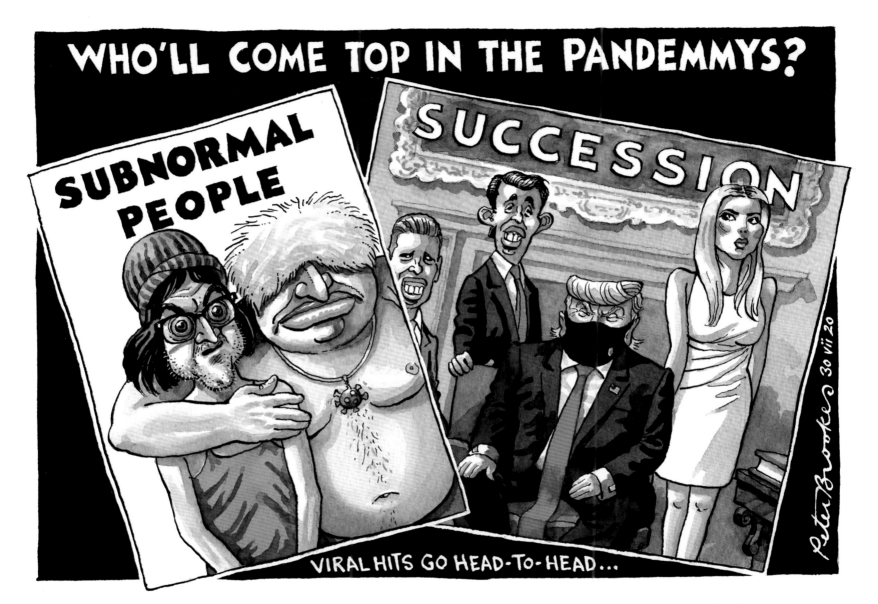

Nominations are announced for the 2020 Emmys. Drama continues to unfold in both the White House and Downing Street over the response to the Covid-19 pandemic.

Robert Jenrick admits he 'regrets' texting Conversative donor Richard Desmond but defends greenlighting the tycoon's housing development despite his decision being found unlawful by reason of apparent bias.

The Kremlin denies any involvement in the attempted murder of opposition leader
Alexei Navalny in the wake of his poisoning with a Novichok nerve agent.

THE GOVT. GUIDE TO MINGLING...

Home Secretary Priti Patel claims two families of four stopping to chat outside would be illegal 'mingling' under the new 'rule of six', but grouse shooting parties of up to thirty are exempt.

Frustrations rise at NHS Test and Trace delays, with reports of people being asked to travel hundreds of miles to obtain a Covid test.

Donald Trump and Joe Biden's first presidential debate descends into a shouting match,
described by one reviewer as 'the political equivalent of a food fight'.

Donald Trump tests positive for Covid-19, recalling his earlier suggestion
that injecting disinfectant could treat the virus.

A rogue fly steals Mike Pence's thunder during the vice-presidential debate.
Donald Trump describes his coronavirus infection as a 'blessing from God'.

Local leaders reject the government's attempt to impose regional lockdown on the north-west, describing the Tier 3 restrictions as treating the north like 'canaries in the coalmine'.

Boris Johnson declares UK–EU trade talks 'over' – a move regarded by EU leaders as political posturing – after French President Emmanuel Macron takes a hard line on fishing rights.

THE UNITED KINGDOM...

The devolved nations' and major regions' differing approaches to coronavirus highlight the tensions
within the UK, with one official criticising Westminster's 'almost colonial mindset'.

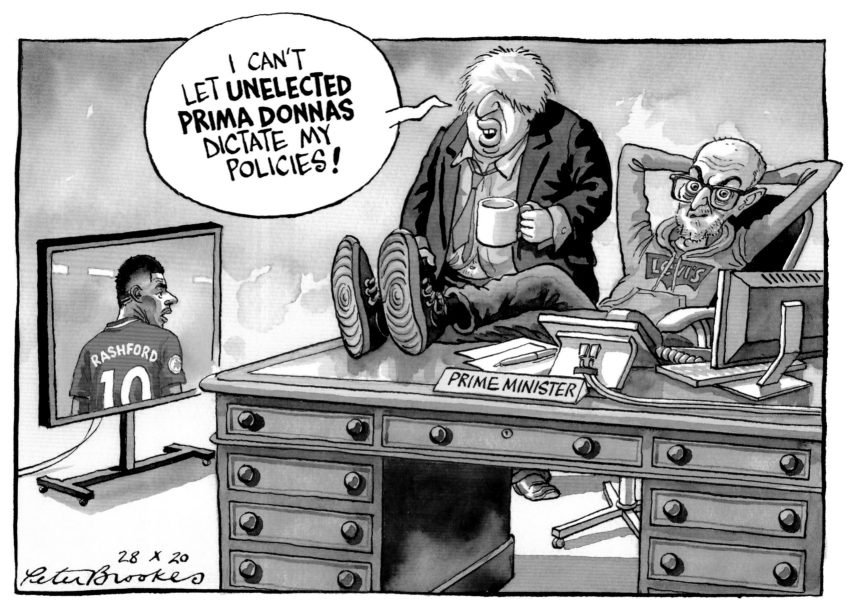

Boris Johnson faces a backlash after refusing to extend free school meal provision over the half-term and Christmas holidays, as footballer Marcus Rashford rallies communities to fight child poverty.

With Joe Biden closing in on the presidency as counting continues, Donald Trump unleashes a barrage of unsourced claims of electoral fraud.

The announcement that Boris Johnson's chief adviser Dominic Cummings will leave Downing Street by Christmas delights many who were angered by Cummings's breach of lockdown rules.

Self-isolating Boris Johnson appears at the first ever virtual Prime Minister's Questions.

Keir Starmer decides to withhold the whip from Jeremy Corbyn the day after Labour's National Executive Committee restores the former leader's membership, reigniting factional tensions.

Boris Johnson refuses to sack Priti Patel after a Cabinet Office inquiry finds evidence that she bullied civil servants and therefore breached the ministerial code, 'even if unintentionally'.

Rishi Sunak faces a backlash after breaking a manifesto commitment by cutting foreign aid spending, prompting Foreign Office minister Baroness Sugg to resign in protest.

Donald Trump reiterates his unfounded allegations of voter fraud but concedes he will leave the White House if the Electoral College confirms Joe Biden's victory.

The Tier 2 rule that pubs can serve alcohol only with a 'substantial meal' causes confusion in government, with Michael Gove swiftly U-turning on his controversial claim that Scotch eggs count as a starter.

The UK becomes the first country in the world to approve Pfizer's Covid-19 vaccine;
Matt Hancock says he'll have the jab on live TV to show it is safe.

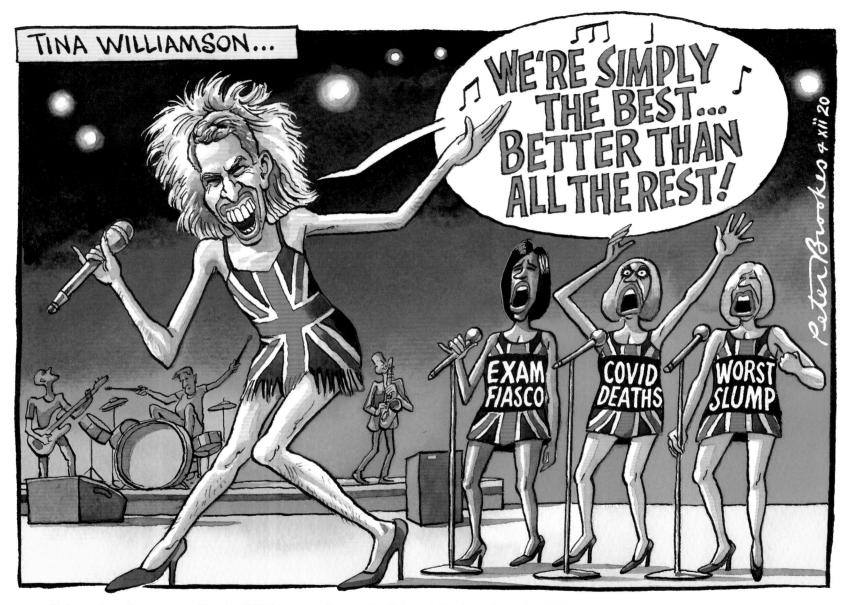

Education Secretary Gavin Williamson is mocked for claiming that the UK approved the Pfizer vaccine first because 'we're a much better country' than others. Tina Turner's new self-help book becomes a global bestseller.

WHITTY'S GHOST

ACKNOWLEDGMENTS TO 'A CHRISTMAS CAROL'

Chief medical officer Chris Whitty warns that Covid restrictions will be required until at least March 2021.

Boris Johnson says a no-deal Brexit is 'very, very likely' as the deadline for
a trade agreement looms. Barbara Windsor dies aged eighty-three.

Jacob Rees-Mogg comes under fire for accusing UNICEF of 'playing politics' by providing food parcels for hungry children affected by the Covid-19 pandemic in the UK.

Boris Johnson raises the UK's coronavirus alert level as the chief medical officers of
the four nations warn of a 'material risk' of the NHS being overwhelmed.

After inciting an attack on the US Capitol by his supporters, Donald Trump belatedly concedes defeat, promising a 'smooth, orderly and seamless transition of power'.

Donald Trump delivers a farewell speech, promising his supporters, 'We will be back.'

Boris Johnson attempts to forge a relationship with incoming President Joe Biden, who previously referred to the PM as a 'physical and emotional clone' of Donald Trump.

Boris Johnson says he is 'deeply sorry' as the UK marks 100,000 coronavirus deaths.

Boris Johnson visits a Scottish vaccine lab to press the benefits of the Union after Nicola Sturgeon promises an independence referendum if the SNP win the forthcoming Holyrood election.

Continental relations become strained when, amid a tense row between the European Commission and AstraZeneca, President Macron claims the British-developed AZ jab is 'quasi-ineffective' on those over sixty-five.

The Vaccine supply in danger:
— or "Merde alors, where's my share?"

ASTRAZENECA

5 ii 21

Peter Brookes — AFTER GILLRAY'S PLUMB-PUDDING —

Discussions over how to distribute vaccine supplies in Europe continue, while claims that the AstraZeneca jab is ineffective in people over sixty-five are refuted by the UK's regulatory agency.

10 ii 21 Peter Brookes AFTER CHAS ADDAMS—

Boris Johnson looks forward to unveiling a 'good news checklist' on lifting
lockdown restrictions as a result of the vaccine rollout.

Health Secretary Matt Hancock announces restructuring plans for the NHS,
while scientists find pigs can play video games with their snouts.

Matt Hancock continues to reveal his plans for NHS restructuring, while detractors criticise attempts to do so while the pandemic is still stretching the system to breaking point.

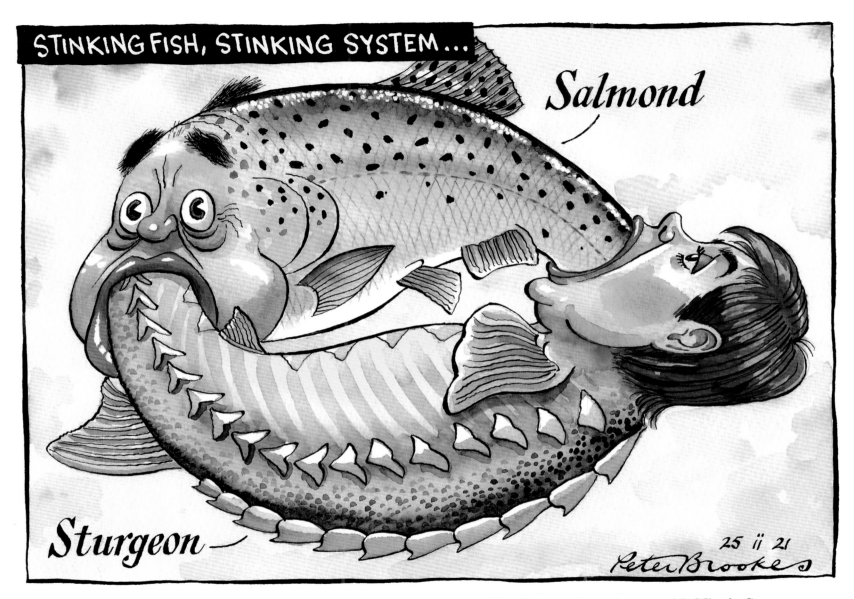

STINKING FISH, STINKING SYSTEM...

Salmond

Sturgeon

25 ii 21

PeterBrookes

The inquiry into the handling of sexual assault claims against Alex Salmond continues, with Nicola Sturgeon dismissing the former First Minister's allegations of a conspiracy against him as 'wild, untrue and baseless'.

Boris Johnson is reported to be considering setting up a charity to fund Carrie Symonds's costly refurbishment of their Downing Street flat.

Rishi Sunak's 2021 Budget fails to reflect Boris Johnson's pledge to reform social care.

The government insists it cannot afford more than a 1 per cent pay rise for NHS staff; the
Home Office pays Sir Philip Rutnam following bullying claims against Priti Patel.

Harry and Meghan's explosive interview with Oprah prompts crisis talks at Buckingham Palace. A UK court upholds allegations that Dubai's ruler orchestrated the abduction and torture of two of his daughters.

Boris Johnson's government commissions a study of the feasibility of a Northern Ireland–Scotland crossing, and the royal family aims for damage control following Harry and Meghan's interview.

Boris Johnson insists Iran's continued detention of Nazanin Zaghari-Ratcliffe following completion of a five-year sentence and Britain's £400 million debt for failing to deliver tanks are 'two entirely separate issues'.

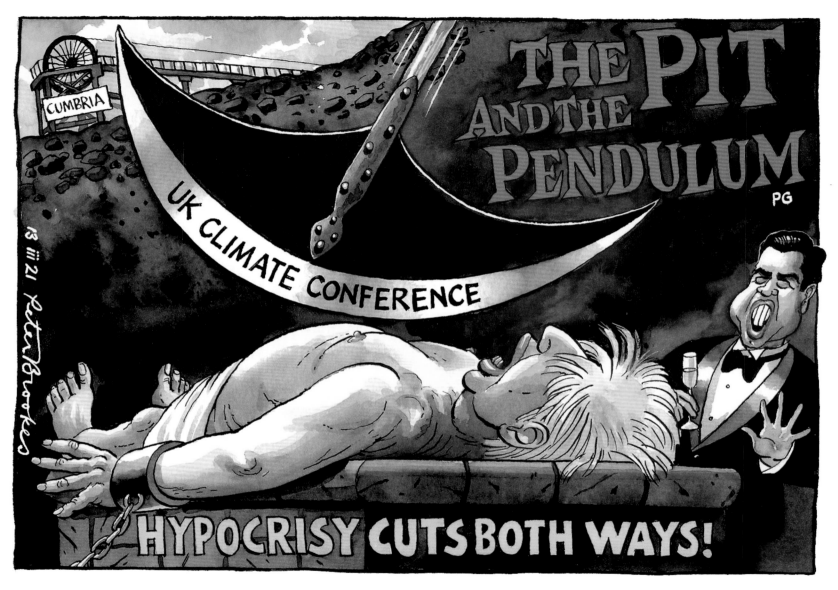

Johnson is criticised for his inconsistent energy policy, including a changeable attitude towards a new coalmine in Cumbria, as the UK assumes the presidency of the COP26 climate change summit.

Europe's vaccine row deepens as several countries pause distribution of the AZ jab pending a European Medicines Agency investigation into blood clots – a suspension critics describe as politically motivated.

Speculation mounts that the Home Office is considering controversial
Australian-style offshore detention centres to deter asylum seekers.

A committee of MSPs concludes that Nicola Sturgeon gave an inaccurate account of her dealings with Alex Salmond during the investigation of sexual assault complaints against the former First Minister.

The independent Hamilton Inquiry clears Nicola Sturgeon of breaching the ministerial code in relation to the Salmond investigation, and Clive Myrie is announced as the new host of BBC's *Mastermind*.

Scotland's 4 per cent pay rise offer to NHS staff increases pressure on Boris Johnson.

A Batley teacher is suspended for showing pupils a cartoon of the Prophet Muhammad, and David Cameron's efforts to secure government support for now-collapsed financier Greensill Capital come under scrutiny.

Reports emerge that David Cameron's lobbying for Greensill included a desert camping trip with Crown Prince Mohammed bin Salman months after the Saudi leader was accused of ordering Jamal Khashoggi's assassination.

Life doesn't reflect art on April Fool's Day.

The World Health Organization criticises Europe's 'unacceptably slow' vaccine rollout, while politicians belatedly try to shore up confidence in the jab. Emmanuel Macron U-turns and announces France's third lockdown.

Boris Johnson sticks to his road map out of lockdown, allowing pubs to reopen, amid warnings from scientific advisers that further easing may spark a third wave.

The UK's vaccine advisory body recommends that under-30s should be offered an alternative
to the AstraZeneca jab, in a 'course correction' to the government's previous advice.

Riots break out in loyalist areas of Northern Ireland, sparked in part by post-Brexit trading arrangements.

The Queen announces the death of Prince Philip, the Duke of Edinburgh, aged ninety-nine.

US climate envoy John Kerry visits Shanghai for talks on cutting emissions amid tensions over China's treatment of the Uighur minority, declared a genocide by the Biden administration.

THE EVOLUTION OF CAM...

ETON   OXFORD   MP   PM

16 IV 21 Peter Brookes

Tory MPs condemn David Cameron's lobbying on behalf of Greensill Capital as the former Prime Minister faces at least three separate inquiries into the scandal.

Britain and France's long-running dispute over fishing rights flares up, with both countries sending naval patrols to Jersey to handle a dawn blockade by French fishermen.

Despite the Conservative manifesto pledge to tackle the social care crisis,
Boris Johnson fails to include a plan in the Queen's Speech.

Prince Harry describes royal life as 'a mix of being in *The Truman Show* and being in the zoo' in an interview to promote his new TV series.

Keir Starmer considers starring in a fly-on-the-wall documentary to reboot
his image. Fans eagerly await the *Friends* reunion special.

Lord Dyson's independent inquiry finds that Martin Bashir lied and used fake documents to secure his explosive 1995 interview with Princess Diana and the BBC's investigation covered up his deceit.

Ahead of the G7 summit, Boris Johnson and Joe Biden sign a new Atlantic Charter, but tensions simmer over the Northern Ireland Protocol as the 'sausage war' threatens post-Brexit trade.

Matt Hancock faces calls to resign after photos emerge of him breaching
social distancing rules by kissing adviser Gina Coladangelo.